_____'s

LEADERSHIP
JOURNAL

Email us at

modernkidpress@gmail.com

to get free extras!

_____

Just title the email "Kid's Leadership"

And we will send some extra

surprises your way!

DATE: S   M   T   W   TH   F   S   ___/___/___

OVERALL TODAY WAS: ☆ ☆ ☆ ☆ ☆

ONE OF THE DAY'S TRIUMPHS:	ONE OF THE DAY'S CHALLENGES:

ONE THING I LEARNED FROM MY TRIUMPH OR CHALLENGE:

TOP GOAL FOR TOMORROW

DATE: S M T W TH F S ___ / ___ / ___

OVERALL TODAY WAS: ☆ ☆ ☆ ☆ ☆

ONE OF THE DAY'S TRIUMPHS:

ONE OF THE DAY'S CHALLENGES:

ONE THING I LEARNED FROM MY TRIUMPH OR CHALLENGE:

TOP GOAL FOR TOMORROW

DATE: S M T W TH F S ___ / ___ / ___

OVERALL TODAY WAS: ☆ ☆ ☆ ☆ ☆

ONE OF THE DAY'S TRIUMPHS:	ONE OF THE DAY'S CHALLENGES:

ONE THING I LEARNED FROM MY TRIUMPH OR CHALLENGE:

TOP GOAL FOR TOMORROW

DATE: S   M   T   W   TH   F   S   ___ / ___ / ___

OVERALL TODAY WAS: ☆ ☆ ☆ ☆ ☆

ONE OF THE DAY'S TRIUMPHS:	ONE OF THE DAY'S CHALLENGES:

ONE THING I LEARNED FROM MY TRIUMPH OR CHALLENGE:

_____

_____

_____

TOP GOAL FOR TOMORROW

_____

DATE: S   M   T   W   TH   F   S   ___ / ___ / ___

OVERALL TODAY WAS: ☆ ☆ ☆ ☆ ☆

ONE OF THE DAY'S TRIUMPHS:	ONE OF THE DAY'S CHALLENGES:

ONE THING I LEARNED FROM MY TRIUMPH OR CHALLENGE:

TOP GOAL FOR TOMORROW

DATE: S M T W TH F S ___ / ___ / ___

OVERALL TODAY WAS: ☆ ☆ ☆ ☆ ☆

ONE OF THE DAY'S TRIUMPHS:	ONE OF THE DAY'S CHALLENGES:

ONE THING I LEARNED FROM MY TRIUMPH OR CHALLENGE:

_____
_____
_____

TOP GOAL FOR TOMORROW

DATE: S   M   T   W   TH   F   S   ___ / ___ / ___ .

OVERALL TODAY WAS: ☆ ☆ ☆ ☆ ☆

ONE OF THE DAY'S TRIUMPHS:	ONE OF THE DAY'S CHALLENGES:

ONE THING I LEARNED FROM MY TRIUMPH OR CHALLENGE:

_____

_____

_____

TOP GOAL FOR TOMORROW

_____

DATE: S M T W TH F S ___ / ___ / ___

OVERALL TODAY WAS: ☆ ☆ ☆ ☆ ☆

ONE OF THE DAY'S TRIUMPHS:

ONE OF THE DAY'S CHALLENGES:

ONE THING I LEARNED FROM MY TRIUMPH OR CHALLENGE:

TOP GOAL FOR TOMORROW

DATE: S   M   T   W   TH   F   S   ___ / ___ / ___

OVERALL TODAY WAS: ☆ ☆ ☆ ☆ ☆

ONE OF THE DAY'S TRIUMPHS:	ONE OF THE DAY'S CHALLENGES:

ONE THING I LEARNED FROM MY TRIUMPH OR CHALLENGE:

_____

_____

_____

TOP GOAL FOR TOMORROW

_____

A GOOD LEADER MAKES A PLAN!

WHEN I GROW UP I WANT TO BE A...

_____

I THINK I CAN DO THIS JOB BECAUSE I AM GOOD AT...

_____

_____

SOME THINGS I WILL DO TO REACH MY GOAL:

_____

_____

_____

_____

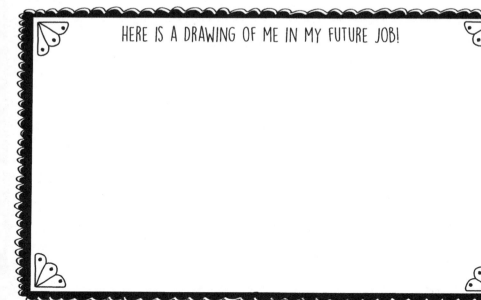

HERE IS A DRAWING OF ME IN MY FUTURE JOB!

DATE: S M T W TH F S ___ / ___ / ___

OVERALL TODAY WAS: ☆ ☆ ☆ ☆ ☆

ONE OF THE DAY'S TRIUMPHS:	ONE OF THE DAY'S CHALLENGES:

ONE THING I LEARNED FROM MY TRIUMPH OR CHALLENGE:

TOP GOAL FOR TOMORROW

DATE: S   M   T   W   TH   F   S   _____ / _____ / _____

OVERALL TODAY WAS: ☆ ☆ ☆ ☆ ☆

ONE OF THE DAY'S TRIUMPHS:	ONE OF THE DAY'S CHALLENGES:

ONE THING I LEARNED FROM MY TRIUMPH OR CHALLENGE:

TOP GOAL FOR TOMORROW

DATE: S   M   T   W   TH   F   S   ___ / ___ / ___

OVERALL TODAY WAS: ☆ ☆ ☆ ☆ ☆

ONE OF THE DAY'S TRIUMPHS:	ONE OF THE DAY'S CHALLENGES:

ONE THING I LEARNED FROM MY TRIUMPH OR CHALLENGE:

TOP GOAL FOR TOMORROW

DATE: S M T W TH F S ___ / ___ / ___

OVERALL TODAY WAS: ☆ ☆ ☆ ☆ ☆

ONE OF THE DAY'S TRIUMPHS:

ONE OF THE DAY'S CHALLENGES:

ONE THING I LEARNED FROM MY TRIUMPH OR CHALLENGE:

TOP GOAL FOR TOMORROW

DATE: S   M   T   W   TH   F   S   ___ / ___ / ___

OVERALL TODAY WAS: ☆ ☆ ☆ ☆ ☆

ONE OF THE DAY'S TRIUMPHS:	ONE OF THE DAY'S CHALLENGES:

ONE THING I LEARNED FROM MY TRIUMPH OR CHALLENGE:

TOP GOAL FOR TOMORROW

DATE: S M T W TH F S ___ / ___ / ___

OVERALL TODAY WAS: ☆ ☆ ☆ ☆ ☆

ONE OF THE DAY'S TRIUMPHS:	ONE OF THE DAY'S CHALLENGES:

ONE THING I LEARNED FROM MY TRIUMPH OR CHALLENGE:

TOP GOAL FOR TOMORROW

DATE: S M T W TH F S ___ / ___ / ___

OVERALL TODAY WAS: ☆ ☆ ☆ ☆ ☆

ONE OF THE DAY'S TRIUMPHS:

ONE OF THE DAY'S CHALLENGES:

ONE THING I LEARNED FROM MY TRIUMPH OR CHALLENGE:

TOP GOAL FOR TOMORROW

DATE: S   M   T   W   TH   F   S   ___ / ___ / ___

OVERALL TODAY WAS: ☆ ☆ ☆ ☆ ☆

ONE OF THE DAY'S TRIUMPHS:

ONE OF THE DAY'S CHALLENGES:

ONE THING I LEARNED FROM MY TRIUMPH OR CHALLENGE:

TOP GOAL FOR TOMORROW

DATE: S M T W TH F S ___ / ___ / ___

OVERALL TODAY WAS: ☆ ☆ ☆ ☆ ☆

ONE OF THE DAY'S TRIUMPHS:	ONE OF THE DAY'S CHALLENGES:

ONE THING I LEARNED FROM MY TRIUMPH OR CHALLENGE:

TOP GOAL FOR TOMORROW

A GOOD LEADER WORKS BEFORE PLAY!

THINK OF A FEW TASKS YOU NEED TO COMPLETE
TOMORROW AND WRITE THEM DOWN
IN THE CORRECT LIST BELOW.

MOST IMPORTANT

LESS IMPORTANT

 GREAT LEADERS SPEND TIME ON IMPORTANT TASKS FIRST!

DATE: S   M   T   W   TH   F   S   ___/___/___

OVERALL TODAY WAS: ☆ ☆ ☆ ☆ ☆

ONE OF THE DAY'S TRIUMPHS:	ONE OF THE DAY'S CHALLENGES:

ONE THING I LEARNED FROM MY TRIUMPH OR CHALLENGE:

_____
_____
_____

TOP GOAL FOR TOMORROW

_____

DATE: S M T W TH F S ____ / ____ / ____

OVERALL TODAY WAS: ☆ ☆ ☆ ☆ ☆

ONE OF THE DAY'S TRIUMPHS:	ONE OF THE DAY'S CHALLENGES:

ONE THING I LEARNED FROM MY TRIUMPH OR CHALLENGE:

TOP GOAL FOR TOMORROW

DATE: S M T W TH F S ___ / ___ / ___

OVERALL TODAY WAS: ☆ ☆ ☆ ☆ ☆

ONE OF THE DAY'S TRIUMPHS:	ONE OF THE DAY'S CHALLENGES:

ONE THING I LEARNED FROM MY TRIUMPH OR CHALLENGE:

TOP GOAL FOR TOMORROW

DATE: S M T W TH F S ____ / ____ / ____

OVERALL TODAY WAS: ☆ ☆ ☆ ☆ ☆

ONE OF THE DAY'S TRIUMPHS:	ONE OF THE DAY'S CHALLENGES:

ONE THING I LEARNED FROM MY TRIUMPH OR CHALLENGE:

TOP GOAL FOR TOMORROW

DATE: S   M   T   W   TH   F   S   ___ / ___ / ___

OVERALL TODAY WAS: ☆ ☆ ☆ ☆ ☆

ONE OF THE DAY'S TRIUMPHS:

ONE OF THE DAY'S CHALLENGES:

ONE THING I LEARNED FROM MY TRIUMPH OR CHALLENGE:

TOP GOAL FOR TOMORROW

DATE: S M T W TH F S ___ / ___ / ___

OVERALL TODAY WAS: ☆ ☆ ☆ ☆ ☆

ONE OF THE DAY'S TRIUMPHS:	ONE OF THE DAY'S CHALLENGES:

ONE THING I LEARNED FROM MY TRIUMPH OR CHALLENGE:

TOP GOAL FOR TOMORROW

DATE: S   M   T   W   TH   F   S   ___ / ___ / ___

OVERALL TODAY WAS: ☆ ☆ ☆ ☆ ☆

ONE OF THE DAY'S TRIUMPHS:	ONE OF THE DAY'S CHALLENGES:

ONE THING I LEARNED FROM MY TRIUMPH OR CHALLENGE:

TOP GOAL FOR TOMORROW

DATE: S M T W TH F S ___ / ___ / ___

OVERALL TODAY WAS: ☆ ☆ ☆ ☆ ☆

ONE OF THE DAY'S TRIUMPHS:

ONE OF THE DAY'S CHALLENGES:

ONE THING I LEARNED FROM MY TRIUMPH OR CHALLENGE:

TOP GOAL FOR TOMORROW

DATE: S M T W TH F S ___ / ___ / ___

OVERALL TODAY WAS: ☆ ☆ ☆ ☆ ☆

ONE OF THE DAY'S TRIUMPHS:

ONE OF THE DAY'S CHALLENGES:

ONE THING I LEARNED FROM MY TRIUMPH OR CHALLENGE:

TOP GOAL FOR TOMORROW

A GOOD LEADER SETS GOALS!

THINK OF A GOAL THAT IS IMPORTANT TO YOU, IMAGINE YOURSELF
ACHIEVING THAT GOAL, THEN DRAW A PICTURE OF IT BELOW.

DATE: S   M   T   W   TH   F   S   ___ / ___ / ___

OVERALL TODAY WAS: ☆ ☆ ☆ ☆ ☆

ONE OF THE DAY'S TRIUMPHS:

ONE OF THE DAY'S CHALLENGES:

ONE THING I LEARNED FROM MY TRIUMPH OR CHALLENGE:

TOP GOAL FOR TOMORROW

DATE: S   M   T   W   TH   F   S   ___ / ___ / ___

OVERALL TODAY WAS: ☆ ☆ ☆ ☆ ☆

ONE OF THE DAY'S TRIUMPHS:

ONE OF THE DAY'S CHALLENGES:

ONE THING I LEARNED FROM MY TRIUMPH OR CHALLENGE:

_____
_____
_____

TOP GOAL FOR TOMORROW

_____

DATE: S   M   T   W   TH   F   S   ___ / ___ / ___

OVERALL TODAY WAS: ☆ ☆ ☆ ☆ ☆

ONE OF THE DAY'S TRIUMPHS:

ONE OF THE DAY'S CHALLENGES:

ONE THING I LEARNED FROM MY TRIUMPH OR CHALLENGE:

TOP GOAL FOR TOMORROW

DATE: S M T W TH F S ___ / ___ / ___

OVERALL TODAY WAS: ☆ ☆ ☆ ☆ ☆

ONE OF THE DAY'S TRIUMPHS:	ONE OF THE DAY'S CHALLENGES:

ONE THING I LEARNED FROM MY TRIUMPH OR CHALLENGE:

TOP GOAL FOR TOMORROW

DATE: S M T W TH F S ___ / ___ / ___

OVERALL TODAY WAS: ☆ ☆ ☆ ☆ ☆

ONE OF THE DAY'S TRIUMPHS:	ONE OF THE DAY'S CHALLENGES:

ONE THING I LEARNED FROM MY TRIUMPH OR CHALLENGE:

TOP GOAL FOR TOMORROW

DATE: S   M   T   W   TH   F   S   ___ / ___ / ___

OVERALL TODAY WAS: ☆ ☆ ☆ ☆ ☆

ONE OF THE DAY'S TRIUMPHS:	ONE OF THE DAY'S CHALLENGES:

ONE THING I LEARNED FROM MY TRIUMPH OR CHALLENGE:

TOP GOAL FOR TOMORROW

DATE: S   M   T   W   TH   F   S   __ / __ / __

OVERALL TODAY WAS: ☆ ☆ ☆ ☆ ☆

ONE OF THE DAY'S TRIUMPHS:	ONE OF THE DAY'S CHALLENGES:

ONE THING I LEARNED FROM MY TRIUMPH OR CHALLENGE:

TOP GOAL FOR TOMORROW

DATE: S M T W TH F S ___ / ___ / ___

OVERALL TODAY WAS: ☆ ☆ ☆ ☆ ☆

ONE OF THE DAY'S TRIUMPHS:	ONE OF THE DAY'S CHALLENGES:

ONE THING I LEARNED FROM MY TRIUMPH OR CHALLENGE:

_____

_____

_____

TOP GOAL FOR TOMORROW

DATE: S M T W TH F S ___ / ___ / ___

OVERALL TODAY WAS: ☆ ☆ ☆ ☆ ☆

ONE OF THE DAY'S TRIUMPHS:	ONE OF THE DAY'S CHALLENGES:

ONE THING I LEARNED FROM MY TRIUMPH OR CHALLENGE:

TOP GOAL FOR TOMORROW

A GOOD LEADER STAYS POSITIVE!

I CAN CHOOSE MY OWN ATTITUDE! COLOR IN ALL OF THE
POSITIVE PHRASES BELOW AND CROSS OUT THE NEGATIVE ONES.

I can figure this out.

This is too hard.

Nobody likes me.

I can always improve.

I give up.

I have more to learn.

I am trying my best.

I can't do it.

This may just take time.

Mistakes help me learn.

DATE: S M T W TH F S ___ / ___ / ___

OVERALL TODAY WAS: ☆ ☆ ☆ ☆ ☆

ONE OF THE DAY'S TRIUMPHS:	ONE OF THE DAY'S CHALLENGES:

ONE THING I LEARNED FROM MY TRIUMPH OR CHALLENGE:

TOP GOAL FOR TOMORROW

DATE: S M T W TH F S ___ / ___ / ___

OVERALL TODAY WAS: ☆ ☆ ☆ ☆ ☆

ONE OF THE DAY'S TRIUMPHS:	ONE OF THE DAY'S CHALLENGES:

ONE THING I LEARNED FROM MY TRIUMPH OR CHALLENGE:

TOP GOAL FOR TOMORROW

DATE: S M T W TH F S ___ / ___ / ___

OVERALL TODAY WAS: ☆ ☆ ☆ ☆ ☆

ONE OF THE DAY'S TRIUMPHS:

ONE OF THE DAY'S CHALLENGES:

ONE THING I LEARNED FROM MY TRIUMPH OR CHALLENGE:

TOP GOAL FOR TOMORROW

DATE: S   M   T   W   TH   F   S   ___ / ___ / ___

OVERALL TODAY WAS: ☆ ☆ ☆ ☆ ☆

ONE OF THE DAY'S TRIUMPHS:

ONE OF THE DAY'S CHALLENGES:

ONE THING I LEARNED FROM MY TRIUMPH OR CHALLENGE:

TOP GOAL FOR TOMORROW

DATE: S M T W TH F S ___ / ___ / ___

OVERALL TODAY WAS: ☆ ☆ ☆ ☆ ☆

ONE OF THE DAY'S TRIUMPHS:	ONE OF THE DAY'S CHALLENGES:

ONE THING I LEARNED FROM MY TRIUMPH OR CHALLENGE:

TOP GOAL FOR TOMORROW

DATE: S M T W TH F S ___ / ___ / ___

OVERALL TODAY WAS: ☆ ☆ ☆ ☆ ☆

ONE OF THE DAY'S TRIUMPHS:

ONE OF THE DAY'S CHALLENGES:

ONE THING I LEARNED FROM MY TRIUMPH OR CHALLENGE:

TOP GOAL FOR TOMORROW

DATE: S M T W TH F S ___ / ___ / ___

OVERALL TODAY WAS: ☆ ☆ ☆ ☆ ☆

ONE OF THE DAY'S TRIUMPHS:

ONE OF THE DAY'S CHALLENGES:

ONE THING I LEARNED FROM MY TRIUMPH OR CHALLENGE:

TOP GOAL FOR TOMORROW

DATE: S M T W TH F S ___ / ___ / ___

OVERALL TODAY WAS: ☆ ☆ ☆ ☆ ☆

ONE OF THE DAY'S TRIUMPHS:	ONE OF THE DAY'S CHALLENGES:

ONE THING I LEARNED FROM MY TRIUMPH OR CHALLENGE:

TOP GOAL FOR TOMORROW

DATE: S M T W TH F S ___ / ___ / ___

OVERALL TODAY WAS: ☆ ☆ ☆ ☆ ☆

ONE OF THE DAY'S TRIUMPHS:

ONE OF THE DAY'S CHALLENGES:

ONE THING I LEARNED FROM MY TRIUMPH OR CHALLENGE:

TOP GOAL FOR TOMORROW

A GOOD LEADER BUILDS OTHERS UP!

EVERY PERSON BRINGS THEIR OWN STRENGTHS TO THE TABLE. WHAT ARE SOME OF YOUR FRIENDS STRENGTHS THAT YOU COULD GIVE THEM AN AWARD FOR? WRITE THEM DOWN AND DECORATE THE AWARDS BELOW.

DATE: S M T W TH F S ___ / ___ / ___

OVERALL TODAY WAS: ☆ ☆ ☆ ☆ ☆

ONE OF THE DAY'S TRIUMPHS:	ONE OF THE DAY'S CHALLENGES:

ONE THING I LEARNED FROM MY TRIUMPH OR CHALLENGE:

TOP GOAL FOR TOMORROW

DATE: S M T W TH F S ____ / ____ / ____

OVERALL TODAY WAS: ☆ ☆ ☆ ☆ ☆

ONE OF THE DAY'S TRIUMPHS:

ONE OF THE DAY'S CHALLENGES:

ONE THING I LEARNED FROM MY TRIUMPH OR CHALLENGE:

TOP GOAL FOR TOMORROW

DATE: S   M   T   W   TH   F   S   ___ / ___ / ___

OVERALL TODAY WAS: ☆ ☆ ☆ ☆ ☆

ONE OF THE DAY'S TRIUMPHS:

ONE OF THE DAY'S CHALLENGES:

ONE THING I LEARNED FROM MY TRIUMPH OR CHALLENGE:

TOP GOAL FOR TOMORROW

DATE: S M T W TH F S ___ / ___ / ___

OVERALL TODAY WAS: ☆ ☆ ☆ ☆ ☆

ONE OF THE DAY'S TRIUMPHS:	ONE OF THE DAY'S CHALLENGES:

ONE THING I LEARNED FROM MY TRIUMPH OR CHALLENGE:

TOP GOAL FOR TOMORROW

DATE: S   M   T   W   TH   F   S   ____ / ____ / ____

OVERALL TODAY WAS: ☆ ☆ ☆ ☆ ☆

ONE OF THE DAY'S TRIUMPHS:	ONE OF THE DAY'S CHALLENGES:

ONE THING I LEARNED FROM MY TRIUMPH OR CHALLENGE:

TOP GOAL FOR TOMORROW

DATE: S M T W TH F S ___ / ___ / ___

OVERALL TODAY WAS: ☆ ☆ ☆ ☆ ☆

ONE OF THE DAY'S TRIUMPHS:	ONE OF THE DAY'S CHALLENGES:

ONE THING I LEARNED FROM MY TRIUMPH OR CHALLENGE:

TOP GOAL FOR TOMORROW

DATE: S M T W TH F S ___ / ___ / ___

OVERALL TODAY WAS: ☆ ☆ ☆ ☆ ☆

ONE OF THE DAY'S TRIUMPHS:

ONE OF THE DAY'S CHALLENGES:

ONE THING I LEARNED FROM MY TRIUMPH OR CHALLENGE:

TOP GOAL FOR TOMORROW

DATE: S M T W TH F S ___ / ___ / ___

OVERALL TODAY WAS: ☆ ☆ ☆ ☆ ☆

ONE OF THE DAY'S TRIUMPHS:	ONE OF THE DAY'S CHALLENGES:

ONE THING I LEARNED FROM MY TRIUMPH OR CHALLENGE:

TOP GOAL FOR TOMORROW

DATE: S M T W TH F S ___ / / ___

OVERALL TODAY WAS: ☆ ☆ ☆ ☆ ☆

ONE OF THE DAY'S TRIUMPHS:

ONE OF THE DAY'S CHALLENGES:

ONE THING I LEARNED FROM MY TRIUMPH OR CHALLENGE:

TOP GOAL FOR TOMORROW

A GOOD LEADER LEARNS FROM OTHERS!

A LEADER IS SOMEONE YOU LOOK UP TO.
WRITE DOWN THE NAMES OF A FEW PEOPLE YOU LOOK UP TO BELOW.

 GO AND TELL THEM WHAT THEY MEAN TO YOU!

DATE: S   M   T   W   TH   F   S   /   /

OVERALL TODAY WAS: ☆ ☆ ☆ ☆ ☆

ONE OF THE DAY'S TRIUMPHS:	ONE OF THE DAY'S CHALLENGES:

ONE THING I LEARNED FROM MY TRIUMPH OR CHALLENGE:

TOP GOAL FOR TOMORROW

DATE: S M T W TH F S ___ / ___ / ___

OVERALL TODAY WAS: ☆ ☆ ☆ ☆ ☆

ONE OF THE DAY'S TRIUMPHS:	ONE OF THE DAY'S CHALLENGES:

ONE THING I LEARNED FROM MY TRIUMPH OR CHALLENGE:

TOP GOAL FOR TOMORROW

DATE: S M T W TH F S ___ / ___ / ___

OVERALL TODAY WAS: ☆ ☆ ☆ ☆ ☆

ONE OF THE DAY'S TRIUMPHS:	ONE OF THE DAY'S CHALLENGES:

ONE THING I LEARNED FROM MY TRIUMPH OR CHALLENGE:

TOP GOAL FOR TOMORROW

DATE: S M T W TH F S ___ / ___ / ___

OVERALL TODAY WAS: ☆ ☆ ☆ ☆ ☆

ONE OF THE DAY'S TRIUMPHS:	ONE OF THE DAY'S CHALLENGES:

ONE THING I LEARNED FROM MY TRIUMPH OR CHALLENGE:

TOP GOAL FOR TOMORROW

DATE: S   M   T   W   TH   F   S   ___ / ___ / ___

OVERALL TODAY WAS: ☆ ☆ ☆ ☆ ☆

ONE OF THE DAY'S TRIUMPHS:

ONE OF THE DAY'S CHALLENGES:

ONE THING I LEARNED FROM MY TRIUMPH OR CHALLENGE:

TOP GOAL FOR TOMORROW

DATE: S M T W TH F S ___ / ___ / ___

OVERALL TODAY WAS: ☆ ☆ ☆ ☆ ☆

ONE OF THE DAY'S TRIUMPHS:	ONE OF THE DAY'S CHALLENGES:

ONE THING I LEARNED FROM MY TRIUMPH OR CHALLENGE:

TOP GOAL FOR TOMORROW

DATE: S M T W TH F S ___ / ___ / ___

OVERALL TODAY WAS: ☆ ☆ ☆ ☆ ☆

ONE OF THE DAY'S TRIUMPHS:	ONE OF THE DAY'S CHALLENGES:

ONE THING I LEARNED FROM MY TRIUMPH OR CHALLENGE:

TOP GOAL FOR TOMORROW

DATE: S M T W TH F S ___ / ___ / ___

OVERALL TODAY WAS: ☆ ☆ ☆ ☆ ☆

ONE OF THE DAY'S TRIUMPHS:	ONE OF THE DAY'S CHALLENGES:

ONE THING I LEARNED FROM MY TRIUMPH OR CHALLENGE:

_____
_____
_____

TOP GOAL FOR TOMORROW

DATE: S   M   T   W   TH   F   S   __ / __ / __

OVERALL TODAY WAS: ☆ ☆ ☆ ☆ ☆

ONE OF THE DAY'S TRIUMPHS:	ONE OF THE DAY'S CHALLENGES:

ONE THING I LEARNED FROM MY TRIUMPH OR CHALLENGE:

TOP GOAL FOR TOMORROW

A GOOD LEADER LISTENS FIRST!

FILL IN THE BLANKS BELOW TO FIND OUT
SOME WAYS YOU CAN BE A BETTER LEADER.

1.) I _____ TO OTHERS BEFORE SPEAKING.

2.) I TRY TO _____ THEIR VIEWPOINTS.

3.) I LISTEN WITHOUT _____ .

WORD BANK

UNDERSTAND

INTERRUPTING

LISTEN

DATE: S M T W TH F S ___ / ___ / ___

OVERALL TODAY WAS: ☆ ☆ ☆ ☆ ☆

ONE OF THE DAY'S TRIUMPHS:

ONE OF THE DAY'S CHALLENGES:

ONE THING I LEARNED FROM MY TRIUMPH OR CHALLENGE:

TOP GOAL FOR TOMORROW

DATE: S M T W TH F S ___ / ___ / ___

OVERALL TODAY WAS: ☆ ☆ ☆ ☆ ☆

ONE OF THE DAY'S TRIUMPHS:

ONE OF THE DAY'S CHALLENGES:

ONE THING I LEARNED FROM MY TRIUMPH OR CHALLENGE:

TOP GOAL FOR TOMORROW

DATE: S   M   T   W   TH   F   S   ___ / ___ / ___

OVERALL TODAY WAS: ☆ ☆ ☆ ☆ ☆

ONE OF THE DAY'S TRIUMPHS:	ONE OF THE DAY'S CHALLENGES:

ONE THING I LEARNED FROM MY TRIUMPH OR CHALLENGE:

TOP GOAL FOR TOMORROW

DATE: S   M   T   W   TH   F   S   ___ / ___ / ___

OVERALL TODAY WAS: ☆ ☆ ☆ ☆ ☆

ONE OF THE DAY'S TRIUMPHS:	ONE OF THE DAY'S CHALLENGES:

ONE THING I LEARNED FROM MY TRIUMPH OR CHALLENGE:

TOP GOAL FOR TOMORROW

DATE: S   M   T   W   TH   F   S   ___ / ___ / ___

OVERALL TODAY WAS: ☆ ☆ ☆ ☆ ☆

ONE OF THE DAY'S TRIUMPHS:	ONE OF THE DAY'S CHALLENGES:

ONE THING I LEARNED FROM MY TRIUMPH OR CHALLENGE:

TOP GOAL FOR TOMORROW

DATE: S M T W TH F S _____ / ___ / _____

OVERALL TODAY WAS: ☆ ☆ ☆ ☆ ☆

ONE OF THE DAY'S TRIUMPHS:	ONE OF THE DAY'S CHALLENGES:

ONE THING I LEARNED FROM MY TRIUMPH OR CHALLENGE:

TOP GOAL FOR TOMORROW

DATE: S M T W TH F S ___/___/___

OVERALL TODAY WAS: ☆ ☆ ☆ ☆ ☆

ONE OF THE DAY'S TRIUMPHS:	ONE OF THE DAY'S CHALLENGES:

ONE THING I LEARNED FROM MY TRIUMPH OR CHALLENGE:

_____
_____
_____

TOP GOAL FOR TOMORROW

_____

DATE: S   M   T   W   TH   F   S   ___ / ___ / ___

OVERALL TODAY WAS: ☆ ☆ ☆ ☆ ☆

ONE OF THE DAY'S TRIUMPHS:

ONE OF THE DAY'S CHALLENGES:

ONE THING I LEARNED FROM MY TRIUMPH OR CHALLENGE:

_____

_____

_____

TOP GOAL FOR TOMORROW

_____

DATE: S   M   T   W   TH   F   S   ___ / ___ / ___

OVERALL TODAY WAS: ☆ ☆ ☆ ☆ ☆

ONE OF THE DAY'S TRIUMPHS:

ONE OF THE DAY'S CHALLENGES:

ONE THING I LEARNED FROM MY TRIUMPH OR CHALLENGE:

_____

_____

_____

TOP GOAL FOR TOMORROW

A GOOD LEADER CREATES HEALTHY HABITS!

ILLUSTRATE A FEW OF YOUR HEALTHY HABITS BELOW.

WHAT IS A NEW HEALTHY HABIT YOU WANT TO START?

DATE: S   M   T   W   TH   F   S   ___ / ___ / ___

OVERALL TODAY WAS: ☆ ☆ ☆ ☆ ☆

ONE OF THE DAY'S TRIUMPHS:	ONE OF THE DAY'S CHALLENGES:

ONE THING I LEARNED FROM MY TRIUMPH OR CHALLENGE:

_____

_____

_____

TOP GOAL FOR TOMORROW

DATE: S M T W TH F S ___ / ___ / ___

OVERALL TODAY WAS: ☆ ☆ ☆ ☆ ☆

ONE OF THE DAY'S TRIUMPHS:	ONE OF THE DAY'S CHALLENGES:

ONE THING I LEARNED FROM MY TRIUMPH OR CHALLENGE:

TOP GOAL FOR TOMORROW

DATE: S M T W TH F S ___ / ___ / ___

OVERALL TODAY WAS: ☆ ☆ ☆ ☆ ☆

ONE OF THE DAY'S TRIUMPHS:	ONE OF THE DAY'S CHALLENGES:

ONE THING I LEARNED FROM MY TRIUMPH OR CHALLENGE:

TOP GOAL FOR TOMORROW

DATE: S M T W TH F S ___ / ___ / ___

OVERALL TODAY WAS: ☆ ☆ ☆ ☆ ☆

ONE OF THE DAY'S TRIUMPHS:	ONE OF THE DAY'S CHALLENGES:

ONE THING I LEARNED FROM MY TRIUMPH OR CHALLENGE:

TOP GOAL FOR TOMORROW

DATE: S M T W TH F S ___ / ___ / ___

OVERALL TODAY WAS: ☆ ☆ ☆ ☆ ☆

ONE OF THE DAY'S TRIUMPHS:

ONE OF THE DAY'S CHALLENGES:

ONE THING I LEARNED FROM MY TRIUMPH OR CHALLENGE:

TOP GOAL FOR TOMORROW

DATE: S   M   T   W   TH   F   S   ___ / ___ / ___

OVERALL TODAY WAS: ☆ ☆ ☆ ☆ ☆

ONE OF THE DAY'S TRIUMPHS:

ONE OF THE DAY'S CHALLENGES:

ONE THING I LEARNED FROM MY TRIUMPH OR CHALLENGE:

TOP GOAL FOR TOMORROW

DATE: S M T W TH F S ___ / ___ / ___

OVERALL TODAY WAS: ☆ ☆ ☆ ☆ ☆

ONE OF THE DAY'S TRIUMPHS:

ONE OF THE DAY'S CHALLENGES:

ONE THING I LEARNED FROM MY TRIUMPH OR CHALLENGE:

TOP GOAL FOR TOMORROW

DATE: S M T W TH F S ___ / ___ / ___

OVERALL TODAY WAS: ☆ ☆ ☆ ☆ ☆

ONE OF THE DAY'S TRIUMPHS:	ONE OF THE DAY'S CHALLENGES:

ONE THING I LEARNED FROM MY TRIUMPH OR CHALLENGE:

TOP GOAL FOR TOMORROW

DATE: S M T W TH F S ___ / ___ / ___

OVERALL TODAY WAS: ☆ ☆ ☆ ☆ ☆

ONE OF THE DAY'S TRIUMPHS:	ONE OF THE DAY'S CHALLENGES:

ONE THING I LEARNED FROM MY TRIUMPH OR CHALLENGE:

TOP GOAL FOR TOMORROW

A GOOD LEADER HELPS OTHERS!

WHAT ARE MY GIFTS? WHAT AM I GOOD AT?

HOW CAN I USE MY GIFTS TO HELP OTHERS?

DATE: S M T W TH F S ___ / ___ / ___

OVERALL TODAY WAS: ☆ ☆ ☆ ☆ ☆

ONE OF THE DAY'S TRIUMPHS:	ONE OF THE DAY'S CHALLENGES:

ONE THING I LEARNED FROM MY TRIUMPH OR CHALLENGE:

TOP GOAL FOR TOMORROW

DATE: S   M   T   W   TH   F   S   ___ / ___ / ___

OVERALL TODAY WAS: ☆ ☆ ☆ ☆ ☆

ONE OF THE DAY'S TRIUMPHS:	ONE OF THE DAY'S CHALLENGES:

ONE THING I LEARNED FROM MY TRIUMPH OR CHALLENGE:

_____
_____
_____

TOP GOAL FOR TOMORROW

DATE: S M T W TH F S ___ / ___ / ___

OVERALL TODAY WAS: ☆ ☆ ☆ ☆ ☆

ONE OF THE DAY'S TRIUMPHS:	ONE OF THE DAY'S CHALLENGES:

ONE THING I LEARNED FROM MY TRIUMPH OR CHALLENGE:

TOP GOAL FOR TOMORROW

DATE: S M T W TH F S ___ / ___ / ___

OVERALL TODAY WAS: ☆ ☆ ☆ ☆ ☆

ONE OF THE DAY'S TRIUMPHS:	ONE OF THE DAY'S CHALLENGES:

ONE THING I LEARNED FROM MY TRIUMPH OR CHALLENGE:

TOP GOAL FOR TOMORROW

DATE: S M T W TH F S ___ / ___ / ___

OVERALL TODAY WAS: ☆ ☆ ☆ ☆ ☆

ONE OF THE DAY'S TRIUMPHS:	ONE OF THE DAY'S CHALLENGES:

ONE THING I LEARNED FROM MY TRIUMPH OR CHALLENGE:

TOP GOAL FOR TOMORROW

DATE: S M T W TH F S   ___ / ___ / ___

OVERALL TODAY WAS: ☆ ☆ ☆ ☆ ☆

ONE OF THE DAY'S TRIUMPHS:

ONE OF THE DAY'S CHALLENGES:

ONE THING I LEARNED FROM MY TRIUMPH OR CHALLENGE:

TOP GOAL FOR TOMORROW

DATE: S   M   T   W   TH   F   S   ___ / ___ / ___

OVERALL TODAY WAS: ☆ ☆ ☆ ☆ ☆

ONE OF THE DAY'S TRIUMPHS:

ONE OF THE DAY'S CHALLENGES:

ONE THING I LEARNED FROM MY TRIUMPH OR CHALLENGE:

TOP GOAL FOR TOMORROW

DATE: S   M   T   W   TH   F   S   ___ / ___ / ___

OVERALL TODAY WAS: ☆ ☆ ☆ ☆ ☆

ONE OF THE DAY'S TRIUMPHS:

ONE OF THE DAY'S CHALLENGES:

ONE THING I LEARNED FROM MY TRIUMPH OR CHALLENGE:

TOP GOAL FOR TOMORROW

DATE: S M T W TH F S ___ / ___ / ___

OVERALL TODAY WAS: ☆ ☆ ☆ ☆ ☆

ONE OF THE DAY'S TRIUMPHS:	ONE OF THE DAY'S CHALLENGES:

ONE THING I LEARNED FROM MY TRIUMPH OR CHALLENGE:

TOP GOAL FOR TOMORROW

A GOOD LEADER CELEBRATES DIFFERENCES!

WRITE THE NAME OF A FRIEND IN THE CENTER OF THE FLOWER, THEN RESPOND TO THE PROMPTS IN THE PETALS.

ONE THING I CAN LEARN FROM HIM/HER:

ONE WAY THAT WE ARE THE SAME:

IN SOME WAYS WE ARE DIFFERENT AND I'M GLAD BECAUSE...

ONE WAY THAT WE ARE DIFFERENT IS:

ONE THING I COULD TEACH HIM/HER:

DATE: S M T W TH F S ___ / ___ / ___

OVERALL TODAY WAS: ☆ ☆ ☆ ☆ ☆

ONE OF THE DAY'S TRIUMPHS:

ONE OF THE DAY'S CHALLENGES:

ONE THING I LEARNED FROM MY TRIUMPH OR CHALLENGE:

TOP GOAL FOR TOMORROW

DATE: S M T W TH F S ___ / ___ / ___

OVERALL TODAY WAS: ☆ ☆ ☆ ☆ ☆

ONE OF THE DAY'S TRIUMPHS:	ONE OF THE DAY'S CHALLENGES:

ONE THING I LEARNED FROM MY TRIUMPH OR CHALLENGE:

TOP GOAL FOR TOMORROW

DATE: S   M   T   W   TH   F   S   _____ / ___ / _____

OVERALL TODAY WAS: ☆ ☆ ☆ ☆ ☆

ONE OF THE DAY'S TRIUMPHS:	ONE OF THE DAY'S CHALLENGES:

ONE THING I LEARNED FROM MY TRIUMPH OR CHALLENGE:

TOP GOAL FOR TOMORROW

DATE: S M T W TH F S ___ / ___ / ___

OVERALL TODAY WAS: ☆ ☆ ☆ ☆ ☆

ONE OF THE DAY'S TRIUMPHS:	ONE OF THE DAY'S CHALLENGES:

ONE THING I LEARNED FROM MY TRIUMPH OR CHALLENGE:

TOP GOAL FOR TOMORROW

DATE: S   M   T   W   TH   F   S   ___ / ___ / ___

OVERALL TODAY WAS: ☆ ☆ ☆ ☆ ☆

ONE OF THE DAY'S TRIUMPHS:	ONE OF THE DAY'S CHALLENGES:

ONE THING I LEARNED FROM MY TRIUMPH OR CHALLENGE:

_____

_____

_____

TOP GOAL FOR TOMORROW

DATE: S   M   T   W   TH   F   S   ___ / ___ / ___

OVERALL TODAY WAS: ☆ ☆ ☆ ☆ ☆

ONE OF THE DAY'S TRIUMPHS:

ONE OF THE DAY'S CHALLENGES:

ONE THING I LEARNED FROM MY TRIUMPH OR CHALLENGE:

_____
_____
_____

TOP GOAL FOR TOMORROW

DATE: S M T W TH F S ___ / ___ / ___

OVERALL TODAY WAS: ☆ ☆ ☆ ☆ ☆

ONE OF THE DAY'S TRIUMPHS:	ONE OF THE DAY'S CHALLENGES:

ONE THING I LEARNED FROM MY TRIUMPH OR CHALLENGE:

TOP GOAL FOR TOMORROW

DATE: S   M   T   W   TH   F   S   ___ / ___ / ___

OVERALL TODAY WAS: ☆ ☆ ☆ ☆ ☆

ONE OF THE DAY'S TRIUMPHS:	ONE OF THE DAY'S CHALLENGES:

ONE THING I LEARNED FROM MY TRIUMPH OR CHALLENGE:

TOP GOAL FOR TOMORROW

DATE: S M T W TH F S ___ / ___ / ___

OVERALL TODAY WAS: ☆ ☆ ☆ ☆ ☆

ONE OF THE DAY'S TRIUMPHS:	ONE OF THE DAY'S CHALLENGES:

ONE THING I LEARNED FROM MY TRIUMPH OR CHALLENGE:

TOP GOAL FOR TOMORROW

Made in United States
North Haven, CT
06 March 2023

33570151R00065